DOT-TO-DOT
FAMOUS FACES

TEST YOUR BRAIN AND DE-STRESS WITH PUZZLE SOLVING AND COLOURING

This edition published by Parragon Books Ltd in 2016

Parragon Books Ltd
Chartist House
15–17 Trim Street
Bath BA1 1HA, UK
www.parragon.com

Copyright © Parragon Books Ltd 2016

Puzzles created by Any Puzzle Media Ltd

ISBN 978-1-4748-3830-6
Printed in China

DOT-TO-DOT

FAMOUS FACES

TEST YOUR BRAIN AND DE-STRESS WITH PUZZLE SOLVING AND COLOURING

PaRragon

Bath • New York • Cologne • Melbourne • Delhi
Hong Kong • Shenzhen • Singapore

HOW TO USE THIS BOOK

Join the dots in numerical order to reveal a stunning work of art on every page! Start at '1' and then draw a line to '2', then '3' and so on, until all dots are joined. The first and last numbers are in **bold**, to help you find the start and be sure when you're finished.

The puzzles are arranged in order of increasing complexity, so they will take anything from 20 minutes to up to a few hours to complete. By the time you get to the end of the book, you will find puzzles with up to 2,000 dots to join, so these might best be solved over a couple of evenings.

Some parts of each puzzle have lots of dots and numbers in a small space, but if you are not certain which dot is attached to a particular number then usually all you need to do is look at the surrounding dots and numbers to work it out. Remember that numbers are also always exactly centred above or to the side of a dot, or touching at one of the four main diagonals to it. They are never at any other position, and are always exactly the same distance from the dot. This means that you can always be certain which dot belongs to which number.

We recommend solving these puzzles using a fine-tipped pen or a very sharp pencil so that you do not obscure unused dots and numbers. There is no need to start at '1', however – you can begin anywhere you like and then fill in the missing bits later if you prefer. If you make a mistake then just carry on regardless, since the line-art nature of each picture is very forgiving, and it's good to make each image your own picture in any case!

Once you've joined all the dots, you could colour in the resulting image for a truly unique piece of art. The perforations along each page allow you to tear out any puzzle, so you could give these to friends or even frame them on your wall.

The back pages of the book provides a small preview of each completed image, so be careful not to look at these in advance if you do not want to spoil any of the puzzles!

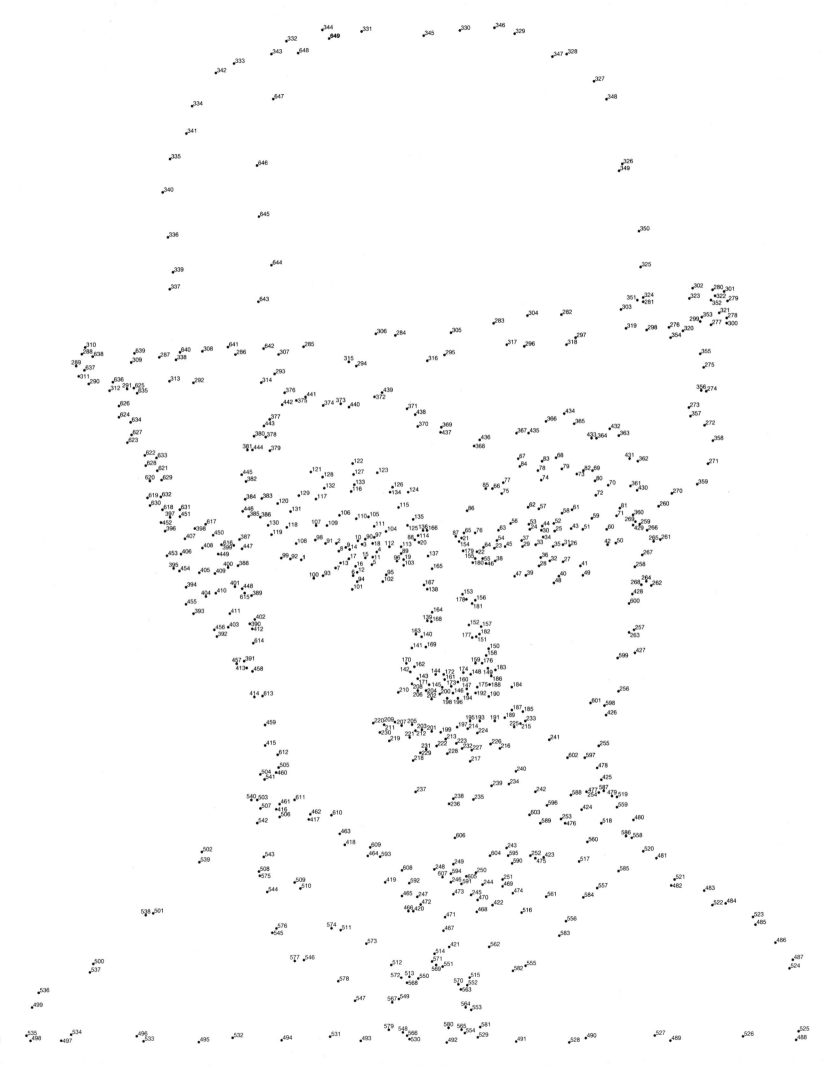

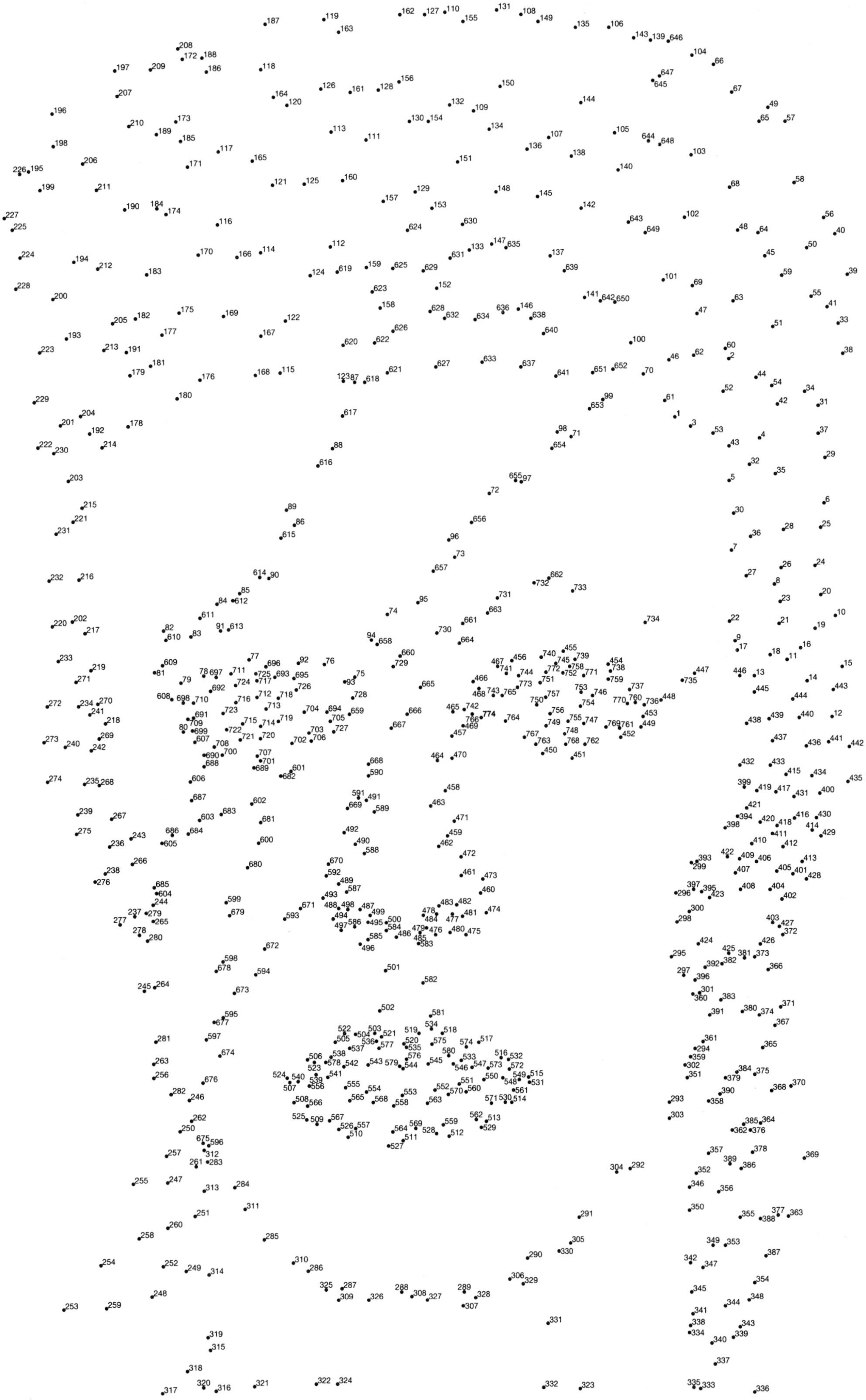

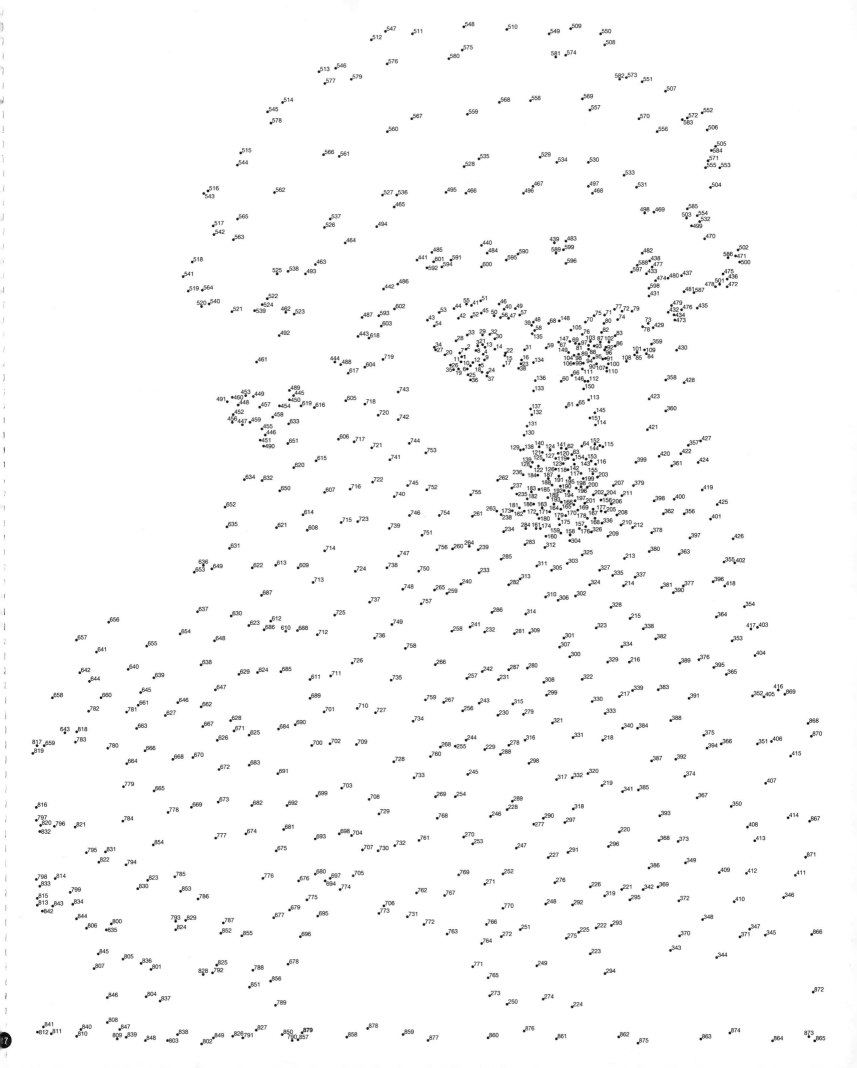

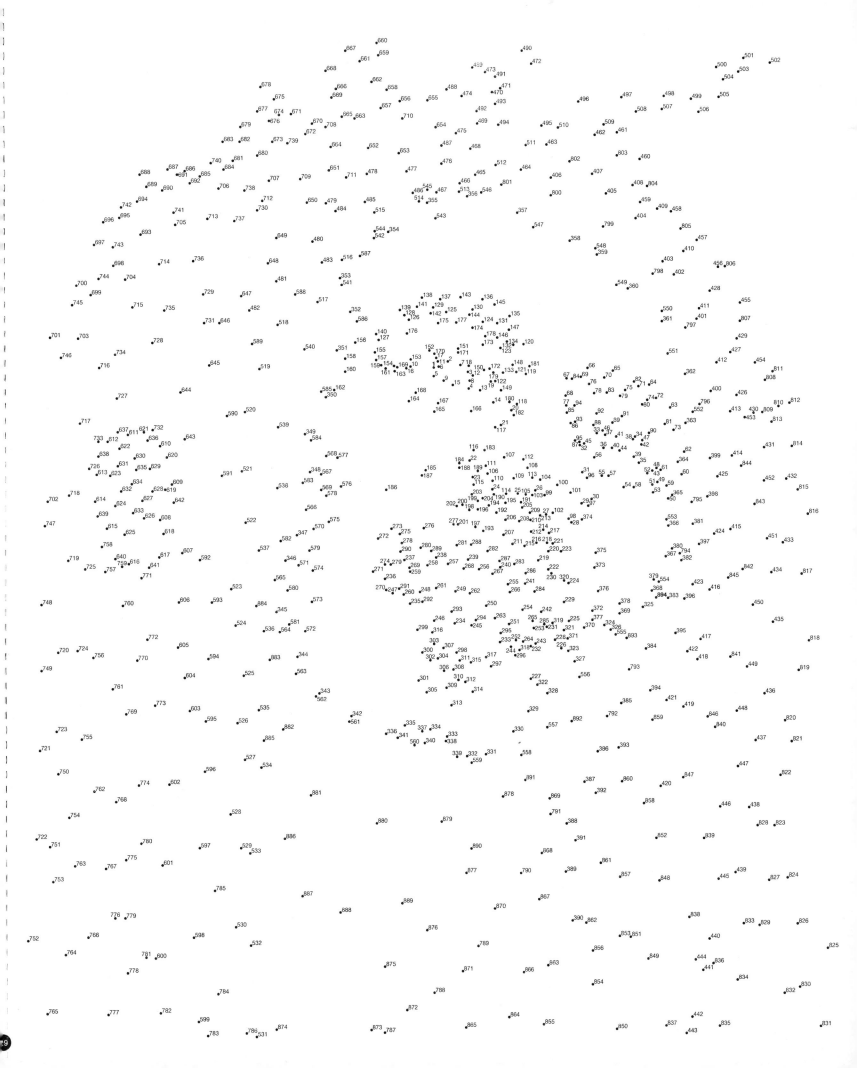

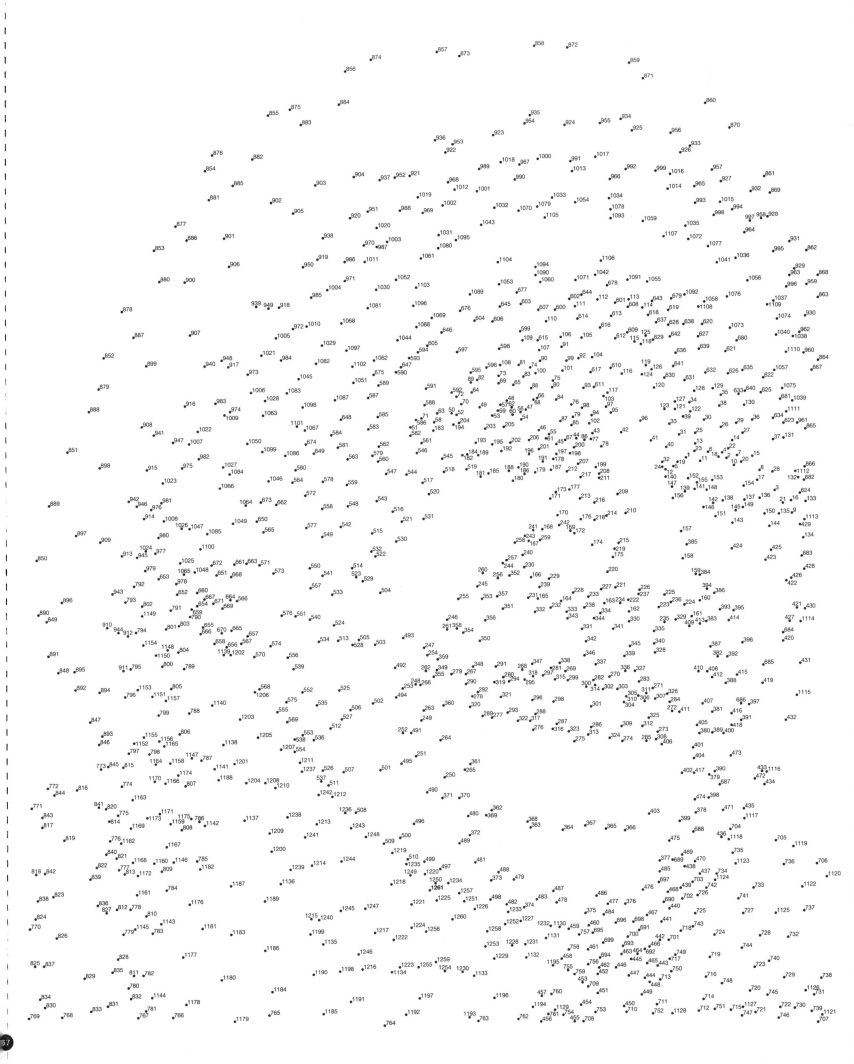

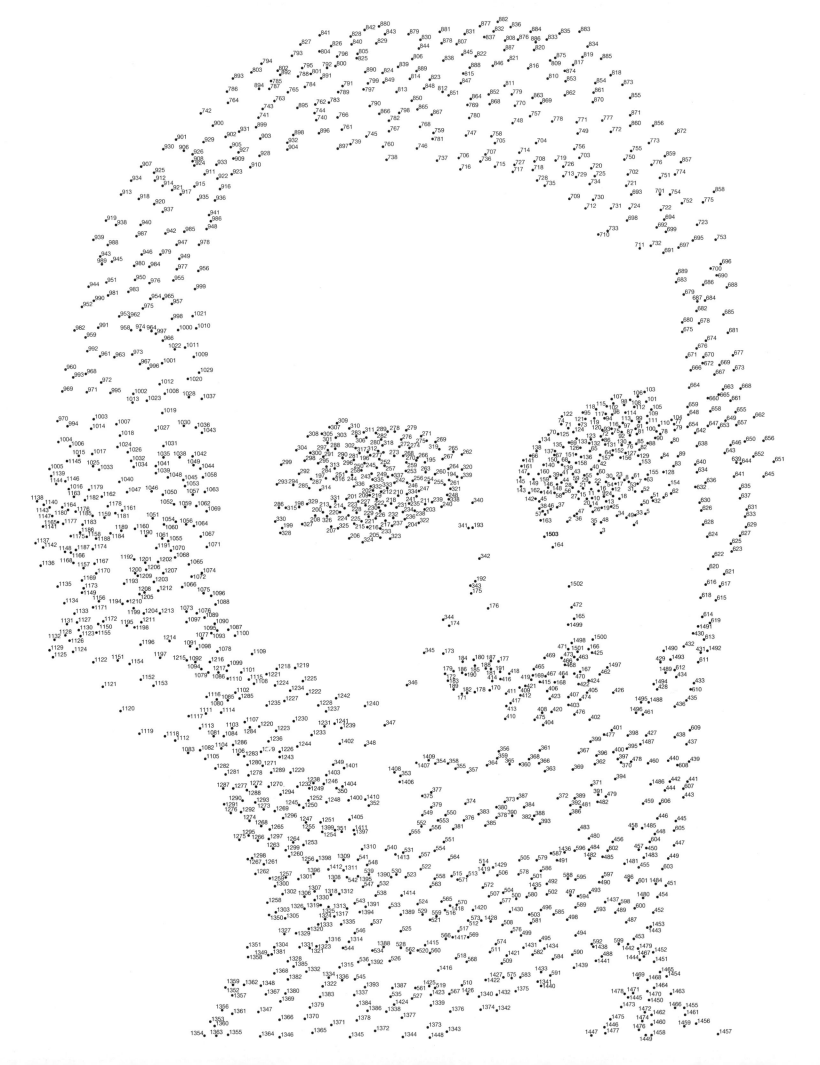

5. Freddie Mercury

7. Martin Luther King

9. Nelson Mandela

11. Audrey Hepburn

13. Charlie Chaplin

15. Bruce Lee

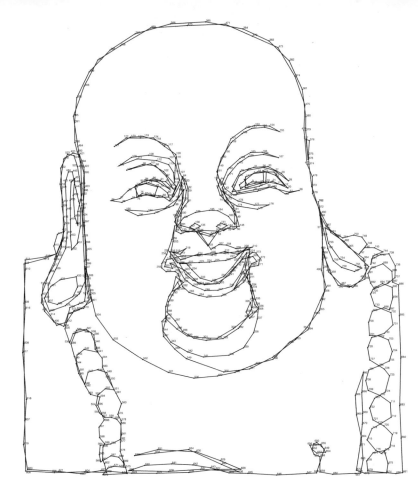

17. Buddha

19. Frank Sinatra

21. David Bowie

23. Cristiano Ronaldo

25. Mick Jagger

27. Leonardo da Vinci

29. Bob Marley

31. Madonna

33. Justin Bieber

35. Winston Churchill

37. Amy Winehouse

39. Che Guevara

41. Albert Einstein

43. Michael Jackson

45. Adele

47. Taylor Swift

49. John F. Kennedy

51. Princess Diana

53. Kurt Cobain

55. Muhammad Ali

57. Elizabeth Taylor

59. Elvis Presley

61. Mahatma Gandhi

63. Marilyn Monroe

65. The Beatles

67. Mother Teresa

69. Bradley Cooper

71. William Shakespeare

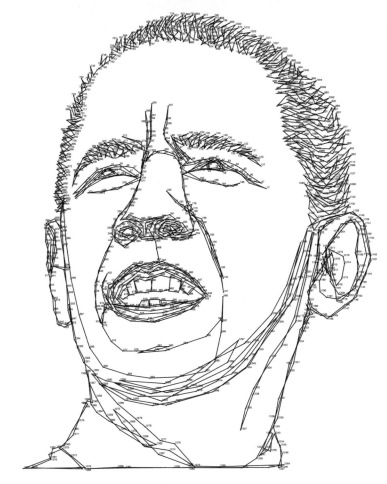

73. Barack Obama

75. Whitney Houston

77. John Lennon

79. Kim Kardashian

81. Abraham Lincoln

83. David Beckham

85. Steve Jobs